The Prophet Returns

Other Books by Kirk Heriot

Who We Are:
A Chronicle of the Ideas That Shaped Our World

Understanding Each Other After 9-11:
What Everyone Should Know
About the Religions of the World

The Prophet Returns

Calm Words for Troubled Times

Kirk Heriot, MD, PhD

LOST≈
COAST
PRESS

Fort Bragg, California

The Prophet Returns

Calm Words for Troubled Times:

https://kirkheriot.wordpress.com/author/kirkheriot/

Lost Coast Press
155 Cypress Street
Fort Bragg, CA 95437
800 773-7782
www.cypresshouse.com
Book Production by Cypress House
Cover Design by Kiersten Hanna

Publisher's Cataloging-In-Publication Data

Names: Heriot, Kirk, 1955- author. | Gibran, Kahlil, 1883-1931. Prophet.

Title: The prophet returns : calm words for troubled times / Kirk Heriot, MD, PhD.

Description: First edition. | Fort Bragg, California : Lost Coast Press, [an imprint of Cypress House], [2022] | Based on The prophet by Kahlil Gibran.

Identifiers: ISBN 9781935448419 (paperback) | ISBN 9781935448457 (ebook)

Subjects: LCSH: Mysticism--Fiction. | Life--Fiction. | Conduct of life--Fiction. | Wisdom--Fiction.

Classification: LCC PS3608.E743 P76 2021 (print) | LCC PS3608.E743 (ebook) | DDC 813/.6--dc23

Library of Congress Control Number: 2021947875

Printed in the USA

2 4 6 8 9 7 5 3 1

First edition

DEDICATION

To my sons, Adam and Neil, that the prodigious words of Kahlil Gibran may enrich their lives. To my father and mother, Henry and Mary, who passed the days in the South Pacific with the boundless wisdom of *The Prophet*. And especially to my mother, for your heart beats with all the love that is described here and in the great work upon which it is based, and your mind races with the thoughts and ideas that are championed in both works. You are the personification of one work and the inspiration for the other.

TABLE OF CONTENTS

FOREWORD

I was first given Kahlil Gibran's *The Prophet* as a gift when I was a teenager—over sixty years ago. It had a powerful impact on me; I recall reading and performing "On Children" and "On Love" at every high school and church opportunity that came my way. It was a book that helped shape both who I wanted to be in the world and how I came to view that world.

My first thought was that it's impossible to channel and revitalize an enduring classic; however, Kirk Heriot's *The Prophet Returns: Calm Words for Troubled Times* succeeds in doing just that. It's done so effectively that it too feels like a gift—especially for these times. The beautifully crafted poetic reflections are a much-needed antidote for the divisiveness and fear so prevalent today when the middle ground of respect and kindness often go uncelebrated.

Once I picked up *The Prophet Returns*, it was hard to put down. I turned to "On Children" first while reciting from memory the opening lines from *The Prophet*: "Speak to us of children: Your children are not your children. They are the sons and daughters of life longing for itself." From *The Prophet Returns*, several lines jumped out at me: "Teach them what you can, but also learn from them, for they are our teachers as well as our students." I so love that he then speaks directly to the children and not just about them. "If the winds can carry love and hope, I send you all I have of both."

The Prophet Returns graces us with wide-ranging wisdom and deep insight born of the reality of our times. In that spirit, there are reflections on women, equality, terrorism, war and peace, divorce, refugees and immigrants, depression, and animals, to name a few.

—Belvie Rooks, co-founder, Growing A Global Heart, and co-author of *I Give You the Springtime of My Blushing Heart*

PREFACE

$\mathcal{K}$AHLIL GIBRAN (1883–1931) was a Lebanese-American writer and artist. He was born to a Maronite (Eastern Catholic) family in the village of Bisharri, in what is now northern Lebanon but was then part of Ottoman Syria. He immigrated with his mother and siblings to the United States in 1895. The best known of his works is *The Prophet*, a collection of twenty-six short prose poems, published in 1923. In *The Prophet*, the wise Almustafa has dwelt in Orphalese for twelve years, but must return to his native land. He answers questions from his admirers prior to departing. In each brief, pithy poem, Gibran offered timeless advice on the problems of life. *The Prophet* has sold more than 50 million copies in more than 100 languages. In *The Prophet Returns*, Almustafa returns for one day to once again speak to the people of Orphalese, both about issues he addressed before, such as love, marriage, and children, and new issues of the modern world, such as divorce, depression, diversity, fundamentalism, and terrorism. My hope has been to write as Gibran would if he could once again give us his wisdom.

THE ARRIVAL

*A*s THE TINY speck came closer, the people of Orphalese could see it was a ship, and those who recalled a man of wisdom began to whisper of possibilities.

As Almustafa disembarked, the few who remembered ran to him with love and greetings, while others wondered if this was the one they had heard of. Almustafa embraced them all, but his eyes searched. Her eyes searched as well, and when they met his, Almitra reached for him. Almustafa took her hand upon his heart, and humanity flowed into humanity in a wordless embrace.

And he said: So often in my native land, I cast my eye lovingly toward you, that I might see you again, even as I loved my own people ever more. For life moves us forward from the old to the new, but is especially sweet when we revisit a fond memory. My foot steps lovingly upon this soil, and my heart fills with delight as I see you. Long have I walked among you in my mind, even though distance upon the sea rendered you invisible.

I have returned to hear again your voices and feel again your thoughts. Speak, my cherished brothers and sisters of Orphalese.

As before, it was Almitra who spoke: Tell us of your life since we saw you, that we may bask again in your wisdom even as we learn of the changes time has brought to you.

And he said: Time has brought changes to my body, but it has not disturbed my thoughts, for these are timeless. In my thoughts, I remain young, and come to you now as I was before.

IT WAS SHE WHO SAID, TELL US ABOUT LOVE, AS YOU DID IN THE DAYS OF OUR YOUTH.

EFORE, HE HAD spoken with a strong voice, but now his whisper carried in the quiet stillness to waiting ears.

And he said: Love is a feeling that your life is made better, richer, fuller, more important, more meaningful, and happier by the presence of another person, an animal, or a passion. Any of these is love. You need only one to savor the meaning and richness of love.

Love is living beyond yourself in an expanded world where moments mean more because we belong to something larger. Love gives hope, greater meaning, and greater joy in life.

When you feel these, love will be at your side and your life will be full.

Do not try to understand love or grasp it or control it or hold it in your hand, for it is the ungraspable spirit of life. Fluid, elusive, and as unknowable as it is eternal. Let love roll between your fingers without understanding or mastery. Simply partake of it and bask in it.

Love is unseen,
hidden,
yet foremost in our thoughts and lives.
It is within reach, but untouchable.
It is the enigma of life.
We cannot describe it
or its effects.
That which transforms our lives
is beyond our language.
It illuminates and warms us,
and changes us,
and enriches us,
and opens our lives.
It is a glow without a source.

Let love shine upon your heart and illuminate your mind without explanation. Indeed, that is its magic. It is stronger than a million stars, but cannot be understood. Yield to love without question, hesitation, or apology. Yield to it in all its forms, and yield to anything that engenders it, human or animal, animate or inanimate. Let love flow over your body, as the sun's warmth flows over your skin.

Do not try to understand how love comes or why it departs, but know that its presence is magical, and even if it departs, it leaves an ember that warms and guides in the darkness of life.

Love is the heart of the world and soul of the universe. From it springs all else. Into it flows all else. Love is a reason to live, an affirmation that gives meaning to life. With love, the sea before us is always calm and the wind behind us is always gentle. Love brings a safe passage and a calm voyage, even to unintended destinations.

> We need not be physically with the one we love
> to feel a gentle caress,
> for love permeates the air
> to seek and find the beloved.
> It overcomes any distance and any time,
> for it lives in our minds.

Love is great joy and great pain. Accept the pain as you relish the joy. Do not try to separate them and partake only of the joy, for this is as futile as separating one side of a coin from the other. The joy and the pain of love are inter-mingled, inseparable, and they come to you together, not as opposites but as siblings. Welcome both into your heart, for though one may be bitter for a while, both enrich you. You cannot reach the summit without the wisdom of the valley.

Caress love even when it has hurt you. It is precisely when you feel like abandoning love, because its pain has overtaken you, that you must embrace it most strongly, for eventually, the joy of love is greater than its pain.

Cherish love over all the superficialities of life. That is the great gift of love—it is a respite from all that is common, shallow, or false. It is a safe space into which we can go to feel the full depth and breadth of life.

Reach for love in any of its forms, and rejoice in love given to others.

> Love emanates from its source
> and travels in the soul of humanity
> to permeate the world.
> Like music played for another,
> but always overheard.

If you have no love in any form, your life is shapeless and ethereal, and your short time on earth is passed without full bloom. But if you have experienced love in any form, when the soft breeze blows past your grave, it will carry memories of the love and passion and meaning of your life.

A SINGLE PERSON, UNACCUSTOMED TO COMPANIONSHIP, SAID, SO PASSION IS A FORM OF LOVE?

AND HE SAID: Passion is a loving devotion, an effort to be better, or to make someone or something better, and it is that effort, not the accomplishment, that rewards. Passion is the melding of all that is good in people—love, curiosity, persistence, kindness. Our hearts and our minds and our spirits all come alive when we feel passion.

Passion elevates life and gives us meaning. It helps us feel anchored and gives us purpose in a changing, mysterious, and sometimes hostile world. Passion helps us to find our voice in the cacophony of life. It gives us the energy of youth, and allows us to feel the wind at our back and the sun in our face.

Before, I told you that work is love made visible. Now, I tell you that passion is love manifest in work. Any passion is love emerging from the blurry midst of life, coming to us as a loving friend and filling us with radiance.

That which gives you peace and purpose sits quietly within you, largely unnoticed. Pause so you can listen to what excites you, to what fills you with meaning. This is the whisper of passion. What do you look forward to? You will know that you have found your passion when doing it fills you with the wonder and amazement and curiosity and joy of a child allowed to stay up past his bedtime. Summon this and place it centrally in your life.

Passion is faithful sustenance when life disappoints and the world seems not to return your love.

Your passion is never a finished work. Shape it ever constantly, ever lovingly, as a sculptor shapes a work that will never be completed, and allow it to be an eternal, ever-changing source of comfort, peace, and purpose.

No success can replace the ecstasy of passion, and no failure can dim the joyous light it casts. If you have passion, you have love, and life has not escaped you.

An older person, who remembered Almustafa, said, Speak to us again of marriage and relationships.

ND HE SAID: Relationships are one manifestation of love. Life can be fully lived without a relationship, but if you are in one, hold it as a gift and a treasure while maintaining and nurturing your own interests, for you are partnering, not merging, with your companion. Nurturing your own passion makes the relationship stronger, as the strings of a violin must be individually in tune before they can come together to make music.

Your relationship is a product of a benign but imperfect world. Do not expect perfection, and do not assume that each partner gives and receives half in all ways. Always give more than what you think is half, and always expect less

10

than what you perceive as half. Love is not about reciprocity, and it does not keep score.

Engage in activities together, have fun together, and make time together a priority, for many relationships are lost simply because they are not actively nurtured, as a plant is lost when not watered.

Make lists of what makes you feel loved, and share these with each other.

Enjoy physical contact, though it need not be sexual.

Try to make the other person's life easier and happier. Love is being happier because someone else is happier.

Be liberal with compliments, for nothing falls so sweetly upon the ear as the soothing words of the chosen one.

Above and before all else, be gentle with criticism. A relationship must be a safe place, and severe or persistent criticism destroys this essential foundation. Make your comments a gentle breeze, not a harsh wind.

Be especially cautious and gentle in what you say and how you react to your companion in times of stress, crisis, or setback, for anger, fatigue, or depression may distort our thinking. It is a tragic irony that when stressed, we may blame those closest and dearest to us, precisely when the partners should comfort and shelter each other. Unkind words or inappropriate criticism, even if born of fatigue or depression, may break a relationship precisely when it is most needed. Guard against this, and if it does happen, the simplest of apologies smooths the roughest of roads. Love means being able to say you are sorry.

Separate growth over the years is to be expected, for no two people are identical or will change in identical ways. Some couples do grow far enough apart to warrant separation, but for most, separate growth will not outshine enduring harmonies.

Unless there is abuse, of which there are many forms, work to make a relationship last, for it is more likely that you can repair a bond with a once and likely still-loved companion than that you will find a better match or be happy alone.

In the fleeting immediate moment, there will always be an attractive person and an exciting possibility, but over the long course of life, your companion likely affords the greatest peace.

When the bonds of love seem diminished, communicate early and freely, for many relationships are lost simply for want of talking.

Anger never helps and talking never hurts.

Seek the counsel of others, for many relationships can be saved simply by a new perspective.

As time passes, let the fire of youth fade and be replaced by companionship, gentle touch, and a communion of minds, for these are far more powerful and far more lasting than the initial physical passion. The enduring strength of a relationship is in gentle, prosaic moments that pass as wisps in time.

Another asked, What of other types of relationships that seem strange to us?

*A*ND HE SAID: My friends, the beauty of love is its simplicity, a simplicity that shines through the darkness of life and illuminates the heart. In a world so bereft of love, let us embrace it and cherish it whenever we find it, in any form it takes. All the world benefits from any love, in any form. Bend your thoughts and your laws to give your children a world with all the love you can find.

ANOTHER PERSON WHO REMEMBERED, SAID, SPEAK TO US AGAIN OF CHILDREN.

AND HE SAID: Children, whose pure hearts beat with nothing but goodness, and whose spirits merge with the earth as rivers into oceans.

With each child, our hopes, our dreams, our sacrifices.

This new life, this expanded world, this feeling of enrichment and beauty.

This connection with the world, this conquest of mortality.

Teach them what you can, but also learn from them, for they are your teachers as well as your students. They teach us what matters in life.

Do not give them your vision of life, or your passions, but help them develop their own. Do not ask them to emulate or surpass you. They are not to be compared to you, for they are unique, and as distinct as one breeze is from another.

Children need love, they need to feel that they are precious to at least one adult, and that they are the center of that adult's world.

So tell them.

Tell them your love goes all the way to the stars and that you will love them for as long as those stars shine.

Be ever interested in the small details of their lives, for those details are the entirety of their thoughts and the extent of their world. Save their cast-aside toys and letters to Santa Claus, for one day these will be as precious to you as they were to them.

Be their foundation when they are frightened, angry, lonely, or sad. Lift them when they fall, dust them off, dry their tears, and make them want to try again. Tell them you will always be near, even if you are far.

And think of them in the silence of the night.

Challenge their minds and expose them to the riches of life, but do not overly push them, for you cannot do with force what can only be done with love. The lessons children need to become happy adults come more quickly from gentle example.

Do not seek for your children to be honor students or graduates of a prestigious university. Your children are not here to win against others, but to live in peace with themselves and in harmony with the world.

Your job is to allow their great journey of life to unfold, not to prepare them for a destination.

Childhood is a time to build experiences, not achievements, for experience is the master teacher. Plant seeds by giving your child experiences, and let those seeds lie dormant. They will one day germinate and enrich your child's sense of belonging in the vastness of life.

The work of a parent is to plant seeds, not to collect fruit.

Your child has a lifetime to amass specific facts, but only a few short years to develop a reverence for learning and knowledge and kindness. Curiosity, veneration of knowledge, lifelong learning, love, compassion, and wise choices are more important than milestones and degrees. If you guide your children to these immortals, all else will fall into place.

Children are our future, but the time of children is not the future; their time is now, for now is the time to give them their future.

Worry less about your children's future.
Just make them happy and secure in the present.
They will find their future
in a world we cannot foresee.
The time of their future
is a foreign language to us,
but it will be their native language.

ONE WHOSE CHILD COULD NOT DO WHAT OTHER CHILDREN COULD DO SAID, SPEAK TO US OF SPECIAL-NEEDS CHILDREN, FOR OUR CRUSHED HOPES ARE MIXED WITH TEARS.

AND HE SAID: Here, nature seems its cruelest, for we seek to establish and guide the next generation so that we can be part of a great journey that began long before us and will continue long after. Our children are our part in the greatest and longest story of our species.

But your sadness stems from what you believe is needed for success and happiness. Freed from the expectations and drudgery that obstruct and obscure, special-needs children have a direct path to all that matters in life.

Think of them as winter children,
as full of beauty as a summer child.
A simple monochromic beauty—
like snow on an ever-branching tree—
that pushes aside the false and
uncovers the essence of life.

In a different way,
and after a second look,
a beauty that rises up to the universe and affirms
life as much as does the beauty of the summer
child.

The miracles of life and love are undiminished. If you love them and seek to keep them safe and happy, you are still part of that great journey.

And your love, and the child upon whom it falls, are the best part of humanity.

THAT PERSON THEN SAID, NOW OUR CHILDREN ARE HERE WITH YOU, A MIRACLE WE NEVER EXPECTED. SPEAK TO THEM, SO THAT YOUR WISDOM WILL PASS THROUGH THEM INTO ETERNITY.

And he turned to the children and said:
If the winds of the earth can carry love and hope,
I send you all I have of both,
and a wish that you will rise up to life
with joy,
though I may not see it,
with laughter,
though I may not hear it,

with love,
though I may not know it.

I wish these for you,
not to receive them in return
but to launch you into life.

Though you will forget me,
perhaps I will not be absent
during your journey through life.
A little part of me will live on in you,
unnoticed.
Perhaps someday you will briefly recall me,
and you will smile,
and a moment of peace will pass over you,
and my hopes for you will be realized.

ALMITRA THEN ASKED, SPEAK NOW TO WOMEN, AS WE REACH FOR EQUALITY.

AND HE SAID: All humanity is richer because of your progress, and the world delights in your movement toward freedom and equality.

Your participation in democracy and social change is crucial, for your reasoning can balance the fear of others.

If you participate in your democracy,
and value love and kindness in significant others,
you will have surpassed your mothers' generation,
made history,
and left your imprint upon all of humanity.

Please join me
in placing kindness
front and center
in every decision,
especially in your choice of companions.

Choose lovers and spouses in whom dwell kindness, curiosity, and the ability to love and nurture. These should make a man more alluring, not less.

For life is short,
companionship is beautiful,
love is rare,
and peace is elusive.

ONE IN MOURNING SAID, SPEAK TO US OF LOSS AND SADNESS.

ND HE SAID: In times of sadness, cherish your memories, that sweet hiatus from the present, that loving mixture of past and present. Nurture your vibrant, glowing, precious, living, breathing memories, which merge sadness and happiness in the strangest of ways. Let them enrich the present, as if happiness had not departed.

Come, sweet memories.
Come and help me build a bridge from the past
to the future.
Come and stand beside me, and comfort me like
a gentle touch or soft smile.

Help me journey into the future,
so that it no longer frightens me,
and so that at some time yet to come
I may be happy again.

Memories are an anchor in times of loss. They allow us to linger in the past just a little longer, until we are able to move on. They bring the past into the present so that we can go forward into the future. Memories are the constancy that makes change possible.

Close your eyes and let your memories flow over you and soothe you. Let them help you build a bridge into the future, and make that future less frightening, so that happiness can again lighten your heart and quicken your pace.

Do not think of memories as reminders of happy moments that can never be again, but as enablers of new happy moments. Make wonderfully comforting visits to the past with your memories, and let them guide you into the future. But do not live in the past with your memories, and do not compare your present with an imaginary present constructed from your memories, for this would be to envy your past, where you cannot live. It is as pointless to envy your own past as it is to envy another person's present.

Happiness is not one pleasant moment made permanent, but a stream of pleasant moments, each ephemeral. Moments of pleasure cannot be permanent, but even as they fade, they are replaced by new flashes of happiness. Your happiness is built from a stream of fleeting moments, each of which illumines your life for a brief moment. Loss is a natural part of that stream.

Life gives and takes, as one drop of water replaces another in a flowing brook. As we stand in a brook, we feel no loss as the water flows away; we feel only joy that it continuously flows around us, as new water replaces the lost.

In times of loss, return to first principles of love, kindness, hope, and curiosity. These will bring you home from any storm, and they are undiminished, though you are without your love. You will tumble through life, for the universe is far stronger than you are, but you will tumble more peacefully if you remember these principles, and hold them as the foundation of your life.

We choose some of life and some of life chooses us. The winds of life may blow us about as the seeds of a dandelion, and we may not know our destination, but with first principles of love, kindness, hope, and curiosity, our travels will be peaceful and we will flourish in our destination, as the seed sprouts in the desert.

Help others after a loss. Nothing gives comfort as much as generosity. Giving in any way leads to receiving in every way. Bend your heart to the last, the least, and the lost, for many have never tasted life in the richness that still courses through your veins, even in your moment of loss. Kindness dispels sadness as love dispels hate and forgiveness dispels anger. Always, and especially in time of loss, be the protector of the weak and the voice of the silent. Nothing diminishes the pain of loss as much as helping others diminish their pain. Understanding the losses of others, the magnitude of which you did not know, will help you understand that the winds of fate have not been unkind to you.

In a time of loss, we feel alone and helpless because the familiar has been taken away. You may feel that life has beaten you down, and in the short run it may have, but in the long run, rise up to life. Accept setbacks as you accept the thorns on a rose, so that you may see clearly the beauty before you.

You may feel a hole in your heart, a bottomless void that forever changes your path in life, but the hole will close, and the heart will heal with a deeper understanding, as a broken bone heals stronger than before.

The peaks of life are filled with happiness, but the greatness of life—forgiveness, love, and growth—flows into the valleys caused by sadness, there to form a pearl.

Happiness will return in a different form, as the richness of summer gives way to the merging colors of fall, then to the gentle whiteness of winter, when the visible white wind sinks softly to the earth, then to the flowering of spring, and then returns, as rich as before.

Do not think "if only": if only this had happened, or if only this had not. Do not put a question mark where life has put a period. Accept the period, then write your own next page.

The roads of life do not flow smoothly into desired, predictable destinations. Rather, they give us an uneven, sometimes tearful journey into unknown places, but unknown places are often richer than our intended destination. Welcome change into your life as you would welcome an uninvited stranger and become better by learning from him. The tragedies of today are the opportunities of tomorrow, and the void that seems endless will become a new foundation.

Do not seek to immediately replace the loss, but rather savor your memories and accept the transition as a unique and valuable part of life. Transitions are not inherently inferior times that must be endured; they are unique opportunities. The hole in your life will heal, and when it does, the reconstitution will be all the richer if you have taken advantage of the unique opportunities of the time in transition.

Do not think only of what is lost, but also of what remains, and the possibilities for the future. Pleasure in the present moment and something to look forward to in the future are the twin pillars of happiness.

Life does what life does. Let time, the slow and silent comforter, work its quiet miracle and gradually return you to life.

ONE WHOSE HEART WAS HEAVY WITH THE SADNESS THAT NO ONE UNDERSTANDS, SAID, TELL US OF DIVORCE.

AND HE SAID: Divorce is a perhaps the cruelest loss, for it is the least expected. Love should be the safest place in life. But like any loss, divorce cannot long disturb the fabric of your life if you accept change, find new opportunities, help others, and return to first principles.

Though you are alone in physical love, you are one with all in spiritual love.

Do not try to understand divorce, for you cannot understand the sting of a bee or the prick of a thorn, but all pass through your life and leave only a scar.

In truth, our lives are lived alone, even if we are coupled, for our thoughts are unique, our fears personal, and our time brief. We may journey partially with another, and feel the deepest of love, but we travel with our own hopes and dreams, as the trees in the forest grow together but do not merge. Love adds to our life, but we cannot merge even with those we love, and their loss need not long strike at the foundation of our happiness.

Earlier, I spoke of baking bread together, but not eating from the same loaf, and of the strings of a lute beating separately, though they quiver with the same tune. Now you bake bread separately, but its taste and nourishment are unchanged. Now you are a smaller and simpler instrument, with fewer strings, but they can resonate with pure and joyous sound.

Whenever love mysteriously dissolves and flows away, it will return, and each time, it will bring new lessons and new peace.

> If love is lost, mourn it, for the loss is real
> and great,
> but it is not permanent.
> The world is full of new loves waiting for you.
> And when you find one, it too will be fluid,
> and may one day flow through your fingers into
> apparent loss,
> only to return richer than before.

Cherish the memories of the relationship. Love can persist and be comforting, nurturing, and soothing even after the lover has gone.

For those of you with children, remember foremost that though an intact family is pleasing to the spirit, the long road to a happy childhood is paved only with the love and attention of our parents. You and your children will navigate the unexpected passage without injury if you make your children feel

> Loved.
> Precious.
> Smart.
> Kind.
> Always safe and happy.

Ask them to make wise choices and let them know you will help them make those choices.

Ask them to tell you of any mistakes they make, whatever they are, for your love is unconditional and you are there to help, not to judge.

> Tell them you are proud of them.
> Tell them you will always be with them, whatever
> the living arrangement or distance.

ONE FOR WHOM SADNESS HAD NOT FADED SAID, TELL US OF DEPRESSION.

AND HE SAID: Depression is a sadness that does not diminish. It is a state of paralysis and numbness in which we no longer recognize our world. We lose hope, and anything that pilfers hope from life is a form of slavery.

> It seems that life has no meaning,
> but in truth, we no longer see its meaning
> because we are confused.
> We look for meaning in the wrong place
> and in the wrong way.

Find anything that gives you pleasure, for even the briefest moment of contentment provides meaning and dispels depression. Fleeting moments of pleasure chisel at depression as rain weathers a rock, and enough of them will return happiness to your life, as the rain makes soil from the rock.

Connect to others in any way, and you will see
that they care more than you realized.
And they can help you.

Though your sadness has lasted long and darkness seems eternal, depression is not permanent.

Look at the world in a new way. Look past what seems unfair or uncaring, and see the small moments of wonder and beauty that you have missed.

The leaves blowing in the wind, sunrises and sunsets, stars, snowflakes.

Ponder these and you will see that the world has
made a place for you,
as it has for the snowflake.

Look at the ground beneath your feet
and the stars over your head.

Look inward to your thoughts, then outward to the little miracles of the world, and light will ultimately appear.

Though you may not see it, the world cares about you. Give the world another chance.

AND THEN ANOTHER OF ORPHALESE SAID, TELL US ABOUT ANIMALS.

A PAINED LOOK CAME upon the old man with the soft voice, and he said: We too are animals, and when we are cruel to animals, we are cruel to ourselves, and to the world of our children, and to the spirit of humanity.

The master spirit of the earth whom I spoke of years ago lies awake and distressed until life in all of its forms is affirmed and held precious.

We have the gifts of abstraction and control of the environment, but we are not smarter or more deserving than animals.

All life is a miracle, and all kindness enriches us. The love of any living creature for any living creature is beautiful, powerful, and seminal. When we revere life in all its forms, our own lives have more meaning. Kindness to animals returns to us through the imperceptible but supreme providence of the universe. Only through kindness can we be the people whom destiny intended us to be. The beauty of life is from feeling love, not from what is loved; it is from giving and receiving love, not whom or what that miraculous exchange is with.

Kindness to animals adds gentleness to our lives, and we need all the gentleness we can get. Nothing enlarges humanity more than a moment of kindness.

When I spoke of loss, I asked you to be the protector of the weak and the voice of the silent. None are weaker or more silent than animals, and when we are kind to them, we become guardians of the earth and protectors of its riches.

ONE WHO REVERED THE TEACHINGS OF THE PAST SAID, WE YEARN FOR THE FAMILIAR IN TIMES OF TURBULENCE, BUT OTHERS OFFER NEW WAYS OF THINKING THAT DISTURB US. SPEAK TO US OF TRADITION.

AND HE SAID: Tradition is a treasure, a timeless gift from the past that gives us comfort and wisdom. Tradition is the foundation upon which knowledge rests and evolves, as the tree grows though the soil is unchanging.

Tradition has produced an infinite and eternal abundance of wisdom that we, in our brief time, cannot surpass, but it cannot speak to all of the challenges and opportunities of the present, because the past cannot perfectly foresee the future. Our path is illuminated by those who came before us; let us revere their wisdom, but knowledge is fluid, and grows. The future can only be better than the past when knowledge, beliefs, and practices change as humanity learns.

Those of the past were giants, but with our own thinking and our own confidence, we can climb upon their shoulders to see farther and reach new understandings.

Let us honor the wisdom of our ancestors by receiving it lovingly and combining it with evolving knowledge into a new world of equality, opportunity, and love, with kindness to every creature.

ONE WHO WAS SEARCHING, SAID, SPEAK TO US AGAIN ABOUT RELIGION.

ND HE SAID: Religions are the great comforter of humanity. They help us traverse the disappointments and uncertainties of life. They offer peace, respite from our travails, and companionship with fellow travelers. Religious beliefs can be among the best of our thought, and religion will be woven into our history for as long as people strive to be better and as long as we hope our children will be kinder.

Believe in the commonalities and wisdom of all religions, and learn from all, for all offer a cornucopia of loving insight. You need not believe in a supreme being, or agree with even their most basic tenets, to be enriched by the world's religions, for all are comforting expressions of the human experience and the wisdom of the ages.

But danger lurks from beliefs that may intrude into and contaminate religions: That this way of thinking is the only correct way; that the use of rational thinking to understand the world or to better our lot conflicts with the will of the Creator; or that any religion has a nobler origin, a superior history, or a greater destiny than other religions. None of these beliefs is integral to any religion. They are all poisonous lies, imposters placed and perpetuated by the misguided, but they can masquerade as part of the religion to near perfection and mislead the unwary.

Disagree with their beliefs as your heart dictates, and guard against contaminating beliefs, but greet all religions with compassion, understanding, and respect.

Whatever your religious beliefs, believe in the courage and potential of people, and let God be a voice within you that gives you hope and peace.

ANOTHER ASKED, WE DO NOT UNDERSTAND THE NEW KIND OF WAR THAT GRIPS THE WORLD. SPEAK TO US OF TERRORISM.

AND HE SAID: We cannot defeat terrorism until we understand the maelstrom that grips the minds of terrorists. These are alienated people, outcasts without a place in the world. They are the huddled masses that no one comforted. Taught to hate and denied opportunity, the terrorist finds hope, camaraderie, and a sense of belonging among peers. The fearful, the excluded, and the angry gain comfort and determination among others who are similarly distressed.

Those whom the terrorist attacks have created a world he can neither understand nor participate in, and they threaten the only understanding of life that he has.

The only solution to terrorism is to sculpt education and opportunity from the darkness that shaped and envelops the terrorist. Opportunity, education, kindness, and a pathway that illuminates attainable alternatives will defeat terrorism. Force must be minimal and patience great.

Fear not and hate not the religion of the terrorist, for this is not the problem. Cruelty is found in equal measure in all religions and cultures. When it is committed by someone of our own faith, we are more tolerant, but when committed by someone of another faith, we are quick to condemn both the perpetrator and his faith.

Terrorists are disproportionately from one religion because recent political and economic developments in the countries that practice that religion foster alienation. Violent acts come from alienation, anger, and mental illness, not from a religion, and always there will be alienated and angry people of all faiths. If you condemn a religion as a cause of terrorism, you will run out of religions to hate before you find peace.

AN UNEMPLOYED PERSON, FEARFUL OF THE FUTURE, SAID, TEACHER, WE HAVE NO JOBS. SPEAK TO US OF FEAR.

AND HE ANSWERED: Fear is the cruelest danger, for it is both ubiquitous and hidden, surreptitiously controlling our lives and stealing reason and compassion. Here I ask much of you, for I ask you to think of the future when you are hungry in the present. Your thinking is weakest, and your heart coldest, when you are afraid, for in fear we seek immediate, certain answers, and are drawn to those who offer them.

Apprehension is normal, but if fear causes us to believe that our problems are caused by a distinct and different group, and that security will return when that group is removed, then we have fallen into the trap of history.

Fear can diminish humanity and all that is human. When you are afraid, grasp the common fabric of humankind and hold it firm. Let your connection to others on the journey of life be the beginning of your own path to sustenance and security.

When we are afraid, we see bright pathways, illuminated by messianic people, that appear to lead to hope and security, but that actually lead to dark caverns filled with hate, anger, war, and all that we must avoid to continue our long journey to a better world. Fear compromises individuality and makes us seek a magical, immediate solution in a special person.

In times of fear, turn away from these imaginings, and nurture kindness and inclusion to bring you security. Security arises from the welcoming breast of humanity, never from the exclusion of part of it. Security arises from the serenity that understanding and kindness bring, never from hate or anger. Let the warmth of humanity—a smile, a touch, a gift—make you less afraid.

Though you feel powerless, stand before the universe and be part of it, without fear, for that which frightens you will pass. In times of fear, hold to first principles of love, kindness, hope, and curiosity, for they will embrace and comfort you and help you avoid the mistakes that fear makes so tempting.

Fear is a cruel and difficult enemy because it robs us of foresight. It thrusts upon us exigencies that seem overwhelming. It deludes us into believing that there is a distinct villain and a distinct hero, and only immediate and decisive action can save us.

Foresight is our greatest gift, but also our most difficult task.

> Hate amplifies fear, but love dispels it.
> Anger amplifies fear, but kindness dispels it.
> Exclusion amplifies fear, but inclusion dispels it.
> In times of fear, let us build bridges, not walls.

In times of fear, you must have a credo. To those who assign blame and offer simple answers, say:

> I believe in humanity,
> in a long march of progress,
> in collective wisdom provided equally by all,
> enriching all.
> I believe in one people,
> with shared purpose,
> in reason and kindness,

in soft words that convey great thoughts,
and in a future made better by a triumph of
reason over fear.

A WORKER, CONCERNED FOR HIS JOB AND AFRAID OF STRANGERS, ASKED, WHAT OF THOSE WHO WOULD FLOOD INTO OUR NATION, TAKE OUR JOBS, AND CHANGE OUR WAY OF LIFE? SPEAK TO US OF REFUGEES AND IMMIGRANTS.

AND HE SAID: Above all, open your heart to those of any faith who flee terror in any of its forms. Refugees are not perpetrators of the terror you fear, but victims of it. They do not bring terror; they flee it. They come in peace and seek only to live, not to hurt.

Refugees will enlarge your society with new ideas. Much of what makes you secure came from those who fled war or terror. Others in the past opened their hearts to the desperate, and all of us reaped rich rewards when inclusion and security came to the frightened. Now it is your turn.

Inclusion always works and exclusion always fails because the radiance of reason is more powerful than the chill of fear.

> Kindness is better than cruelty,
> always,
> even when you are afraid—
> especially when you are afraid.

If you fear and shun refugees, you allow the real terrorists to steal your reason and your humanity. Could they have a greater victory?

Build bridges, not walls. You cannot wall out others without walling out your heritage, your commonality, your compassion, your humanity, and your identity. It is the tragedy of the past and the heartbreak of the present that people see differences instead of similarities. The belief in "otherness" has caused a river of tears in our history.

We are all passengers on this planet, with similar lives and a shared destiny. We owe kindness, generosity, and grace to each other.

Let the warmth of humanity shine upon these sad and frightened people. Have compassion so that others may have life. Open arms and a kind heart make the world safer and richer for all.

Your stomach is not made full by anger, nor is it made empty by kindness.

It is time to embrace those who flee what you fear and say to them: You have experienced sorrow beyond tears. Come now to love beyond words.

ONE WHO WAS DIFFERENT AND HAD NOT BEEN ALLOWED TO PARTICIPATE IN THE FULL GLOW OF LIFE BECAUSE OF THAT DIFFERENCE, SAID, SPEAK TO US OF DIVERSITY AND EQUALITY.

AND HE SAID: Inequality is tragic for all of us. Grieve for the poems, the paintings, the music, and the ideas that those denied full inclusion might have given us. We all lose when anyone is denied the warmth of life in any form, and we all gain when the doors of opportunity swing open for everyone.

We exclude because we fear or hate.

Hate comes from fear, and fear comes from ignorance.

Fear and hate so virulent

that whole groups of people are targeted,
then children are taught to hate,
and forever the cycle continues.
Hate and fear are the assassins of humanity.
With them, history repeats,
and we live on a circle.
We must break the cycle
and live on a line, not on a circle.

A small amount of knowledge sweeps aside the
ignorance that sustains fear and hate,
and replaces the circle with a line.

We all belong to humanity, not to any of its subsets. Each person is a unique manifestation of humanity's oneness. All who share this planet with you have a story to tell. Cherish diversity and you will be magnified by the collective wisdom of the human experience. Diversity and differences create unity and strength, as wood is stronger if made from thin sheets whose grain runs in different directions.

Now is the time to learn history's greatest lesson. Now is the time to bring the whole of humanity under the shield of equality, to make a bold leap that will put our mark upon this moment in history. Now is the time to hear all of the voices of humanity in their radiant fullness and unite into a single people, embracing diversity in all its myriad forms without fear. Now is the time to shine the light of belonging on the whole of humanity, and to let that gentle glow be unbroken and unconditional.

A CITIZEN DISILLUSIONED WITH THE DEMOCRACY HE ONCE CHERISHED SAID, OUR LEADERS HAVE CONSTRAINED MINDS AND IMPOVERISHED SPIRITS. SPEAK TO US OF GOVERNMENT.

AND HE SAID: Democracy requires leaders who understand problems and their causes, and who can think in the long term to find solutions. This requires those who empower them to have these skills. When the people do not understand, those they elect will also be ignorant. The failure of leaders is from failure of the people. Your leaders are put in power by the fear and anger of their supporters, and by the apathy of those who know better.

The path to improvement begins with understanding that the people fail not from lack of intelligence, but from lack of opportunity and security. The people fail when fear and anger prevail over reason, when short-term necessities prevent long-term foresight, and when they cannot foresee the consequences of their action or inaction.

To have better leaders, work for people who understand cause and effect and can think in the long term and participate in democracy even when the benefits take time to emerge. Work for the educational opportunities that create more informed people. Work for the security of people, for security diminishes fear and anger, allowing reason to come to the fore. Opportunity and security reduce the attraction of simple solutions, and bring the patience and understanding needed to formulate permanent solutions.

Your ineffective government has sprung from your incomplete participation. Participate in your government, even if you feel disillusioned, for only you can make it better. Turn toward, not away from, what angers or distresses you. Enter into it, be part of it, and improve it. Let your participation be the instrument of change and the foundation of democracy.

Good choices require foresight and the ability to see beyond immediate circumstances. When the mind and the spirit are free, humanity is unchained, and the people will choose better leaders. The mind and the spirit are restrained, and foresight curtailed, in those who are overtaken by their immediate situation. Always, there will be the uninformed and the fearful, who through no fault of their own cannot make good choices. For a democracy to survive and bring a better world, those who are not benighted must participate fully. Democracy dies when the uninformed have no opposition.

The ability of people to govern themselves is not a yes-or-no question; it is a conditional question. The answer is yes if we participate, and if we are provided with education and security so that we can think beyond the demands of the present, into the future, and choose wisely.

Progress is always uneven. Courage is mixed with timidity, ignorance is mixed with insight, and apathy is mixed with heroism. For all its setbacks, disappointments, and reversals, the long march of human history inches toward greater understanding and humanity. Be part of this march. Bend during a storm, and know that reason cannot long be hidden.

Do not allow short-term setbacks to diminish the singular vision and unique gift of democracy—that the people, together, ultimately have the wisdom to make a better world.

And you yourself have been apathetic and ignorant.

A GENEROUS PERSON SAID, WE ARE SAD FOR THOSE WHO HAVE LITTLE. SPEAK TO US OF POVERTY.

AND HE SAID: Poverty is the destroyer of dreams. It robs us of opportunity and hope. Its long shadow casts darkness upon its victims even after it departs. Until those who hunger in the present and fear for the future are safe in the bosom of humanity, we are not triumphant upon the earth.

No one chooses poverty through idleness, and few can escape its grasp without help. That help must be lasting and have multiple components—education, jobs that pay a fair wage, transportation, childcare, family planning—and a sufficient subsidy for a long enough time to allow those components to work together for substantive and permanent change. Poverty persists because you have never addressed it with a long-term plan that continuously provides all of these essentials.

You cannot end poverty with money alone, for you have many seeds to plant among the poor so that they can acquire all that is necessary to face life. Money alone, without viable seeds for the future, is money wasted, and this you have done in abundance; but neither can you end poverty without money, because much support is needed until your seeds germinate and bear fruit.

Stipulations that cannot be met are equally futile. You must think of seeds for the future instead of demands for the present.

A YOUNG PERSON, READY TO REACH OUT TO LIFE, SAID, SPEAK TO US OF THE ARTS. ARE THEY ESSENTIAL TO LIFE IN THIS AGE?

ALMUSTAFA'S EYES WIDENED, a joyful peace fell upon his face, and he said: Artistic expression in its myriad forms is the accumulated wisdom of humanity put into oral, written, audible, visible, or tangible form. The arts give shape and strength to the human spirit and meaning to life. They are the mark of the universe upon humanity and the mark of humanity upon the universe.

The arts allow us to step away from the mundane and live for a moment on a higher plane, in a better world with greater meaning. The arts soothe our hearts and illuminate the path to kindness. In the noise and distractions of life, the arts remind us what matters, what to be grateful for, and what to hope for. They are the translation of the beauties and mysteries of life into a universal language that makes us pause and think and feel, then begin again, renewed.

We all struggle to make sense of life, of why we are here, and why we are taken away so quickly. Art is a great place to go to make sense of life. The arts teem with lessons for life and nourishment for the mind, as the earth teems with nourishment for the body.

Any form of art may move us with its power, or by allowing us to eavesdrop on its whispers.

The arts push aside the cloak that obscures the abundance of life. They allow us to leave this world for a moment and live in another, better world, where we can be inspired, live beyond ourselves, and glimpse the sublime.

Only the arts can move the veil that conceals what truly matters, and permit the gentle glow of emotion to lovingly infuse our lives. That glow—that elusive, subtle glow, so easily missed—is who we are. Do not pass through this world without feeling its warmth.

We are the only species whose deliberate actions can make the lives of our children better and richer. The arts both chronicle and shape those actions. The arts are the language of our history and the story of our progress.

Among all our endeavors, only the arts can show us the many ways in which we can be injured, and illuminate our fragility, both individually and collectively. Only the arts can show ourselves to ourselves, and highlight that the human spirit is exceedingly delicate but also profoundly resilient. For this alone we should thank them and treasure them and teach them.

The arts allow us to understand and express who we are, what we stand for, and whom we want our children to be. The arts invisibly define and envelop the tapestry of our lives. They make us more comfortable with our individualism and with our differences from others. To be without them is to be without a pulse, to lose vibrancy, and to live in a formless mist.

The arts chronicle the tragedies and resilience of history, and allow us to learn from the past to make a better future. The arts express great ideas that we may not yet be able to fully embrace, and highlight a path that we may not yet be able to traverse.

The arts pour a foundation that will withstand the storms of the present and the future. They open vistas for a better present and a richer future. The arts make us stronger, more productive, and happier. They are the expression of the possibilities and potentials of the mind.

The arts are a home, a safe haven that has preserved the wisdom of the past and grows as each generation adds to it. An ever-growing, ever-comforting home that is anchored in bedrock and soars into infinity, preserving and offering the best of life. To partake of the arts is to enter this home, feel its soothing embrace, explore its infinite rooms, and to know life in a new and richer way.

The arts are mentors and trusted companions from every culture and every age. Whatever has happened to you, however you feel, however bad it seems, someone has been there before you and has recorded comforting thoughts in some form. It might be a work of visual art, music, or literature, but someone, from some time, has been where you are and recorded thoughts and feelings that will soothe you. This is art.

With art, we can live beyond ourselves to touch the richness of life and the infinity of the universe. Art changes us from a speck in an indifferent universe to a glow in a welcoming universe. With the arts, we can hold hands with the world.

Nothing rewards us as richly and in as many ways as the arts. The arts speak to all of us, for all of us, that we may all listen and learn and love together.

The arts are the voice of humanity,

and the voice of history.

They are the voice of the poor, of the sick, of the

oppressed, of the forgotten, of the silent, of the

last, the lost, and the least.

With the arts, we can hear all of humanity, and

share in the full and rich human experience.

You have done wondrous things since I last visited you, but where is your soul? Where is your tenderness? The arts are your soul and your tenderness and your voice. Those who scoff at the arts scoff at the air even as they breathe.

A STUDENT SAID, SPEAK TO US OF LEARNING AND CREATIVITY.

ND HE SAID: Knowledge is the hope of humanity. Our species and curiosity are intimately linked and will survive or perish together. Revere knowledge, seek it, find it, use it, relish it, and pass it on. Believe in the power of the mind and the comprehensibility of the universe, and let curiosity guide you to explore and to cherish knowledge simply for its beauty.

What you learn from your home is greater than what you learn from school, and what you learn from your journey through life is greater than either, for only your journey can teach you who you are.

Collect experiences, not objects. What matters in life cannot be touched or seen, but experience nourishes the spirit, and memories teach and enrich.

Grow throughout life, but remain a child in your wonder and curiosity, for curiosity explored is the fire that ignites all learning.

Mentors are wonderful and inspiring. Emulate revered individuals, for they illuminate the world around us and the path before us. Let the esteemed sharpen your vision, but do not let them be your eyes, for anything seen with your own eyes, even vaguely, will be clearer to you than anything seen through the eyes of another. You need not equal those you admire; it is better to fall into giant footprints than to walk around them.

But even as you cherish esteemed mentors, make your finest teachers the great heritages of history, not individuals. The collective best of humanity can impart far more than even the greatest of individuals. Be guided by heritages, such as ancient Greek exploration, Muslim scholarship in the Middle Ages, the Western Renaissance, the Jewish reverence for learning, the march of compassion, the triumph of the rational, the worth of all individuals, the long-overdue improvement in the treatment of women and children, and the possibility of lifelong growth. These are the master teachers.

Learning is an oasis. The more you understand, the more opportunities you have to escape the mundane world and drink from an oasis of peace, tranquility, and happiness. Along the road of life, learning brings sanctuaries that provide refreshment, rejuvenation, inspiration, perspective, and joy. The more you understand, the more oases will permeate your life and quench the thirst that afflicts so many.

The human experience has many forms, all rich and comforting. Absorb as many varieties of our achievements as you can, for all enlarge your life and comfort your spirit. Learn a little about science and history and all of the arts and the major religions, so that you can sit beside other people, from other places and times, and feel the oneness of humanity. A little knowledge dispels abundant ignorance. You will be richly rewarded for only a little work.

Ignorance is not to be despised or feared, for it is both unavoidable in the present and correctable in the future. Gracefully acknowledge ignorance, so that it can illuminate what you should learn, as a trusted teacher guides you. Ignorance approached intelligently is the path to knowledge.

Do not fear mistakes, for these are master teachers. Mistakes are learning experiences, not commentaries on your worth. And though it is difficult, neither fear embarrassment as you learn, for this is temporary, and nowhere in life is the exchange of loss for profit greater than in a little embarrassment during learning. Be more afraid of perfectionism than of mistakes or failure.

Diplomas and degrees are wonderful for the world and pleasing for the holder, but they do not measure true learning. It is a tragedy that diplomas and status often bring more conceit than wisdom. Arrogance is a poor incubator for innovation. A degree is an opportunity to learn, not a license to be arrogant, and even the most educated must walk the streets of life to grasp its meaning.

Meticulous works of scholarship are always welcome, but the problems of our time are not caused by a lack of detailed knowledge. Rather, they arise from a lack of basic knowledge. The finest education comes not from a prestigious university but from the experiences of life and quiet, persistent reflection and study over many years. Scholarship is a marathon, not a sprint, and while others will inspire and guide us throughout our lives, it is a journey we must take alone. Scholarship is a lifelong voyage of self-discovery.

Creativity is learning applied to life in new ways. The stuff of genius is not a flash of brilliance by a single person with superhuman abilities, but a slow march of the soft voices and small steps of many. You can be a contributor if you have the courage to think afresh.

Creativity is the combination and application of old ideas in a new way. To be a creator, you must have a large worldview and be unencumbered by tradition and protocol. You must divest yourself of the need for perfection and recognition, and be willing to question the most basic concepts you were taught, for what you seek may be well hidden in a small recess, accessible only by traversing paths that others shun.

Creativity may take many forms, but you must follow your own voice. It is better to walk alone and unguided along a difficult path that inspires you than to follow others along an easy and familiar trail. Through your cuts and bruises, you will know yourself and feel the richness of the world. To create is to begin anew and to fall and to fail and to question and to cry and to persist with your own voice.

It will take you years to find your own unique voice, and you will never find it completely. Do not be disturbed by this, because the search for your voice is the joy and the essence of life. It is more important to find your voice than to find an audience.

It is better to speak with your own voice to the emptiest of rooms than with the voice of another to an audience of any size.

A TEACHER, A BUILDER OF THE FUTURE, ASKED, HELP US TO BETTER GUIDE OUR STUDENTS.

*A*ND HE SAID: Impart passion and curiosity, not knowledge. Your students have a lifetime to learn the subject you teach, but you have a limited amount of time to convey the love of knowledge and engagement with life that can speak flexibly to them, throughout their lives, in any situation.

Good education fills minds. Great education opens minds. The filled mind is prepared for the foreseen, and for the tasks for which it was filled; the open mind, fired by passion, is prepared for all the unforeseen challenges of life.

No one knows the course of your student's life. If you simply fill a student's mind, a door may close behind your teaching, because the job is thought to be completed. But if you open a student's mind with a passion for learning, the door remains open, and life will teach your student in a thousand ways neither of you imagined.

A HUMBLE PERSON SAID, SPEAK TO US OF SUCCESS.

ᴀɴᴅ ʜᴇ sᴀɪᴅ: There is only one definition of success— being happy.

Success does not come from money or possessions, and its hallmarks cannot be seen or heard or held. Success comes from the integration of first principles—love, kindness, hope, and curiosity—into your daily life. Hold these eternal foundations fast to your heart and put them foremost in all your dealings, and you will be happy. You will always have the permanence of the intangible.

Whatever you do for a living, be proud of it, do it well, and try to do it better.

Meet the world in friendship, even if you must bow to do so. Do not be angry at the world's imperfections. Accept them with peace, and quiet understanding. For all its flaws, the world was made by billions of brave and dedicated people who merit your respect. Do not be blinded by rage or benighted by ignorance.

Be inspired by the famous and the great, but remember that most heroes are unknown, and walk unseen among you. Quiet heroes care for loved ones without complaint. They comfort children. They stop for the poor and listen to the uneducated. They pass like air beside and around us, silent, unnoticed, lifegiving. If you want to feel the pulse of humanity and the heartbeat of the world, look for these quiet heroes. Listen to them, then strive to be one, with silent courage. Your small victories gather no fame, but they deepen your life and enrich the world. This is success.

Be willing to fail, for there is no other way to explore and to learn. Failures and disappointments do not obstruct the road to success; they pave it. Success comes from failure as surely as the dawn follows the night.

Blend constant development with an eternal childhood, and strive to fulfill your childhood dreams, for being a child throughout life keeps the mind supple. Experience should simplify life, and make clearer that which matters. Good minds add complexity with experience, but great minds subtract it. Never lose the two great characteristics of childhood: curiosity and a sense of humor.

Seek not to achieve, but to experience, for always, life will be too vast for your skills, and always, there will be others through whom you can experience and enjoy what you cannot do. Do not lament what you cannot do; cherish what you can experience.

Though we may feel uniquely incapable and unlucky, both our failures and our disappointments are universal.

Do not think of those who may appear more successful. Your only task on the road of life is to enjoy the journey, not to compare yourself to others. We are all different, though we all follow the same path. Your life will differ from another's as the droplets in a waterfall differ, though they all fall to the earth.

Be gentle with yourself and with others, for stress and anger detract from our lives in equal measure. You cannot be at war with yourself, and you cannot be at peace with yourself without knowing who you are. You must hear yourself to learn who you are, and it is only with gentleness that you can hear the soft voice inside you. Your own voice rises and is clear when you treat yourself as you would have others treat you.

Take pleasure in what you have done, especially in little moments of kindness, even as you aspire to do more.

Do not seek the love of others. Seek only to sit in harmony beside them and in serenity with yourself, for love is not sought and found; it emerges from softness, as the morning emerges from the dawn.

At the end of your life, there will be only three questions: Did you love someone or something in some way? Were you kind? Were you happy?

A SCHOLAR, WISE AND KIND, BUT FILLED WITH THE SADNESS OF BEING IGNORED, SAID, TELL US OF REJECTION.

And he said: As you learn, you will want to teach,

but others will not be taught.

As you understand, you will want others to fol-

low you into your wisdom,

but they will not.

Most will not take your gifts.

Your passion and your wisdom will fly, unheeded,

into the night.

They will not drink from the fountain you have
so carefully prepared for them.
They will die of thirst even as you offer water.
You will hurry to others not with an open hand
to take, but with a filled hand to give.
You will become a different kind of beggar, beg-
ging to give rather than to receive,
but none will take.

Do not be distressed or angry, for those who ignore you
are benighted by a lack of educational opportunities or overcome by the demands of their immediate circumstances.
You must understand their circumstances, even if they cannot understand your message. Do not misconstrue rejection
as malice, and do not allow it to disturb your serenity, your
belief in the miracle of life, or your trust in the fundamen-
tal benevolence of the world. Accept any setback, and *learn*
from it if you can, but *judge* life in the overall.

The human mind is the gift of the universe and the luck of
our species, but a blameless misfortune of birth and life has
deprived many of the ability to understand and the opportunity to learn. We all need a set of beliefs to give us confidence and security. An unwillingness to listen is actually an
inability to hear, arising from a lack of opportunity. Those

who reject you, or who form and cling to unreasonable beliefs, are not stupid. They are simply unlucky because they were unable to develop a rational worldview and cannot relinquish the beliefs that comfort them. They are prisoners, not adversaries. They build walls around their own lives, not around yours.

In the presence of fear, anger, hatred, or ignorance, speak truth with softness in your voice, kindness in your heart, and a belief that you will eventually be heard.

Speak to the future as well as to the present, for the day will come when your words and thoughts are heard, even if that day is beyond your lifetime.

And remember that you too have ignored wise advice.

A VISIONARY, DENIGRATED AND MARGINALIZED, SAID, MASTER, WHAT DO WE DO WHEN WE ARE DISPARAGED? SPEAK TO US OF CRITICISM.

*A*ND HE SAID: Even the strongest among us feels the sting of criticism, for all of us are fragile, longing for the sweet elixir of praise, not the bitter tonic of reproach. Even loving suggestions may injure us.

After a moment of pain and sadness, ponder the criticism and ask if there may be validity. If the criticism is made in anger, arrogance, or intent to hurt, ignore it, for wisdom and guidance do not come in those forms. If your effort has not received respect, ignore the one who criticizes, for all of us deserve respect, and no one has ever learned from contempt. If your finest, longest, and deepest reflections affirm your course, then hold that course fast and firm, for it is your own voice speaking to you.

But if you receive gentle comments made with respect and based on wisdom, and if, with the passage of time, they settle into your mind with serenity, then integrate them into your thinking, as a baker adds a new ingredient to nearly finished bread, though the bread was already savory.

Speak with your own voice, but allow that voice to grow and change and be influenced by the wisest and kindest among you, for always there will be new and different ideas from which you can learn.

ANOTHER SINGLE PERSON, FOR WHOM COMPANIONSHIP WAS UNCOMMON, SAID, SPEAK TO US OF SOLITUDE AND LONELINESS.

AND HE SAID: Loneliness is a painful feeling of detachment when we crave the warmth of belonging. Loneliness is a feeling of separation, not just from other people but from the world. It is a feeling that we do not belong. It is a loss of purpose.

In times of loneliness, find passion in any of its forms. Passion excites us, fills us with purpose, and unites us with the world. Nothing dispels loneliness as much as passion.

Even when alone, you live in the company of all humanity, past and present. Feel the pulse of humanity and the presence of people you will never meet, but from whom you cannot separate, all sharing the commonalities of life with you, all stumbling with you, all feeling triumphs and defeats. Open an imagined dialogue with your unseen fellow travelers, and let your connection to them imbue you with a sense of belonging and peace that flows joyfully into your heart, making its beat stronger even as it beats alone.

Cultivate and treasure friends, for others bring us happiness, but it is only when we are alone that our spirit is at rest, our mind free, and our thoughts unrestrained. Do not fear solitude, for it brings peace. Let it envelop you, softly and slowly, in gentleness.

When you are alone in quiet stillness, let your thoughts come and fall upon you in silence, as snowflakes fall silently in the forest, and let them cover you in beauty, as snowflakes cover the forest in beauty.

> Meet the world with eyes that are open, that you
> may join it
> and be joyful with it
> and love it
> and learn from it.
> But sometimes close your eyes,
> that you may find all that is within you.

Let the world be your orchestra,
accompanying you,
but you are the soloist,
and the melody is yours.

Trust the world and let it touch you.
But trust yourself more and let your touch upon
yourself be the gentlest.

Embrace silence as you do solitude. The sounds of
the world are familiar and comforting, but silence is a
golden peace.

ONE WHO WAS FEARFUL OF DEATH, AND ANOTHER WHO WAS FEARFUL THAT A WAY OF LIFE MIGHT BE FOREVER LOST, CAME FORTH AND SAID, "TELL US ABOUT PLAGUES."

AND HE SAID: Plagues disrupt life in the present and in the future. Beyond the immediate apprehension, uncertainty—the enemy of serenity—pervades, and we fear our lives will be forever changed, even after the plague passes.

Know that the plague is temporary and be ever mindful of a better future. Call again upon memories, as you do after a loss, and let them guide you, for the plague will pass as surely as the future becomes the past.

Think again of the flowing stream whose water is never constant. During a plague, the stream runs with cold and bitter water, but warm and soothing water will soon flow past you again.

Past generations were called to far greater threats, for a far longer time, with far greater loss, than you will be in a plague. Though you may feel powerless, you are empowered by the collective wisdom and courage of the ages.

A plague is the most unwelcome of the uninvited strangers, but opportunities lurk even in the sadness and fear. Live life with an introspective spirit, a slower pace, and a gentler soul. In times of plague and uncertainty, let the first principles of love, kindness, hope, and curiosity once again guide you and be the compass by which you steer.

Let togetherness have a new meaning. Though you are separated from others, you are together in the heart and mind of humanity. Take care of others, for comforting others brings the greatest comfort to ourselves. Have hope, be kind, take care of each other. Love, kindness, goodwill, and humanity spread further in the wind than any virus. Let history record a time of kindness, and let that kindness be the supreme gift of the present to the future.

In a plague, the real danger is loss of our humanity, and the real defense is in little acts of kindness. Be a quiet hero, for it is the unseen and unchronicled labors of quiet heroes that will ultimately defeat the plague.

There will be fear, and that fear is stronger than the virus. But reason and love are stronger than either.

Do not let a plague take your humanity. If it does, you will have no home to return to when it is over.

A LISTENER EXPRESSED A COMMON CONCERN: WE WORRY ABOUT THE FUTURE. TELL US HOW TO LIVE IN THE PRESENT.

AND HE SAID: Beyond reasonable precautions, do not be concerned about difficulties that have not arisen. Most unfortunate events that we imagine will never happen, and of those that do, most cannot be planned for and will ultimately be inconsequential.

Enjoy the present moment without excessive concern for something that is unlikely, inconsequential, and beyond your control. Let trouble unfold and be clear before you address it. You do not carry an umbrella or snow shovel on a sunny day.

The future is beyond your control, but the present is a miracle within your grasp. Enjoy the miracle of life a little each day.

Laugh a little each day.
Remember a little each day.
Love a little each day.
Hope a little each day.
Dream a little each day.

Learn from the past, but live in the present and look forward to the future without fear.

The past is not ours to change.
The future is not ours to know.
But the present is ours to live.

AND THEN ALMITRA, WITH DIMINISHED ENERGY OF THE BODY, BUT UNDIMINISHED ENERGY OF THE MIND, SAID, SPEAK TO US OF OLD AGE.

WITH A GENTLE touch of her hair, a warm touch through which flowed the memories and dreams of decades, he said: I have spoken before of the uninvited stranger. Welcome old age into your life as you would that stranger. Though it takes from you some of youth's quickness, what matters most remains, and is augmented. Old age is a surrender of the trivial for a greater understanding of the profound. Do not be distressed by this exchange. It is long overdue.

You may feel a lack of fulfillment and a reduced sense of belonging. Transitions are difficult, and reduced vitality is a heavy burden. But the passages of life give as much as they take. All stages of life offer fulfillment, but in different ways. Let life show you the pathway to fulfillment and belonging at each stage.

Hope, love, and passion are never beyond you, and with them, the depth and breadth of humanity will never elude your grasp.

Though the time of your future is short, let it be rich with hope—for yourself, your loved ones, and your world. Hope expands your life out of the present and into the future. Hope connects you to the world, though you may be physically alone, and to the future, though it may be brief.

Love is a river that flows constantly, albeit with ever-changing water. We are briefly young and quickly old, but love is integral to life and does not leave us until life itself departs.

Remember that passion is a form of love that is always available to you, even if you are old or alone or weak. Passion softens aging because it excites us and fills us with purpose. Many age prematurely and more cruelly because of a loss of passion. Find something you are passionate about—perhaps something you passed by quickly in your youth, perhaps something you longingly thought of during your middle years—and learn more about it.

As you age, you will become observers in some parts of life in which you were previously participants. Do not be distressed by this, for observation is participation. Indeed, you have been observers in most parts of life all along. Remain passionate about some part of life so that you feel a sense of full participation in its miracle.

Loneliness is the enemy of old age, and many age more severely because they do not have the companionship that is integral to the preservation and blossoming of the mind. As much as you can, go out and meet the world in any way that gives voice to your passion.

You may have retreated from the world, and some of it may move too quickly for you, but you remain intimately a part of it. Live with smaller scope and smaller reach, but undiminished passion. Travel a narrower road at a slower pace, but still see its wonders with youthful eyes.

> Though you are no longer swift and agile,
> or as quick with the new,
> and those who return your glance are few,
> imagine and dream and think and create.
> Find new worlds to explore,
> even if they are smaller and previously unnoticed.

Who is to say if your life is diminished or simply different?

Old age is climbing a hill. You will be winded, but the view is wonderful.

As you age, thank the world for your brief sojourn with it, and for the wonderful moments and pleasant memories it has given you. Wish it well and ask only that it be as kind to your children as it was to you.

And when your life is over or has lost its meaning, when your yesterdays are completed and your tomorrows come no more, let it go without regret or envy. Be grateful for your moment in the sun, and for a richness that outshone so many.

Go gently into death without sadness or resentment. It will be as if you were not yet born, and what sadness or pain do you remember from before your birth?

A SOLDIER, VICTORIOUS BUT INVISIBLY AND INDELIBLY INJURED, SAID, TELL US OF WAR AND PEACE.

AND HE SAID: War injures all, even the victorious, in ways unseen. Posttraumatic stress disorder will invariably affect everyone who participates in war, for suffering—experienced, inflicted, or witnessed—forever disturbs the human spirit.

There will always be people, countries, ideologies, and events you disagree with and that may indeed be tragic and shameful. These are not grounds for war. Other than a direct attack or an imminent genocide, there are no grounds for war. Even in these situations, take care that you strike the true aggressor, and that your action will bring about enduring change, not simply revenge, for revenge only enlarges and makes permanent the consequences of a wrong that could have passed without disturbing your foundation.

And after the war, when you leave
and take your invisible wounds with you,
what of the place you leave behind?

It is no better, for that which you sought to rectify arises from a cascade of enigmas of individual minds and collective consciousness and cannot be corrected by your good intentions or your might.

All you have are grieving survivors on both sides, injured in myriad ways, no closer to peace, understanding, or kindness.

For you cannot give the world kindness with guns.

One Who Had Been Wronged Said, Speak to Us of Anger.

And he said: Anger is normal, and not to be banished or held in shame, but to be blended with compassion and understanding, so that it is only a part of you and never your master.

Place the wrongs perpetrated upon you in context. You will encounter a few people who will make your journey harder than it needs to be, but you will encounter many more who make it easier than it might have been. The gentle stroke of the kind is more frequent, and more lasting, than the sting of the cruel.

It is better to have the soul of a poet than the heart of a warrior. Take as your models Gandhi, King, and Mandela.

All of us are fragile. Those who have hurt you have done so because they have themselves been hurt. If you seek revenge, you perpetuate the cycle, but if you forgive, you break the cycle, make the world a little better, and achieve a far sweeter victory. Only the victim can break this cycle.

It is better to be the last victim than the first avenger.

Anger destroys only the one who feels it, never the intended target. When you feel anger, you simply complete the perpetrator's crime for him. Only by forgiving those who have wronged you can you reclaim your life from anger. Forgiveness is for you, not for the perpetrator. Because forgiveness is for you, you need not believe that the perpetrator deserves forgiveness—you need only believe that you deserve peace.

Forgiveness is the most difficult form of kindness.

The fire of love and forgiveness, though difficult to stoke, always burns hotter and brighter, and shines upon all more constructively, than the fire of hate and revenge.

> If you hurl rage at evil,
> the abyss will swallow you both.
> But if you cast light into darkness,
> the glow will suffuse the world.

Forgiveness dispels anger because love is stronger than hate. As we must be kind for ourselves as much as for the creatures to whom we are kind, so we must forgive for ourselves as much as for a perpetrator. Forgiveness and kindness must be the twin pillars if our brief time is to have the greatest possible meaning. Without them, our time is passed in anger and cruelty, and it is as if we never lived at all.

When you are upset or angry, base your actions on first principles and second thoughts. Many battles are better lost quickly than won slowly. And when you must fight, do so without anger or hatred for your adversary, for your adversary's course may have been determined by factors beyond his control.

Finally, in your anger, ask if you have hurt another, for we are all—victim and perpetrator—a mixture of good and bad. It is more important that you correct the wrong you did to others than that you avenge the wrong done to you.

What you despise in another, you will see in yourself, and neither of you should be hated.

ANOTHER LISTENER THEN SAID,
SPEAK TO US OF EVIL AND FREE WILL.

E HESITATED, AND then spoke with particular softness: My cherished brothers and sisters, on this we must think anew. Evil may appear to be a deliberately malicious exercise of free will, but the human mind is as delicate as it is complex, and the development of free will requires three foundations, all hidden in the mist, that we must unveil and be always mindful of:

A nurturing environment when we are young;
Security;
An absence of mental illness.

When there is apparent free will that has been poorly exercised, we will find that one of these three foundations is absent.

If our early environment nurtures us, teaches us, and gives us the self-esteem to believe we can control our destiny, we can attain free will. But if our early environment is abusive, hostile, unsupportive, or affords minimal opportunities, our moral compass will be without sustenance, and the roots needed to anchor our spirit will be forever elusive. Are we to believe that children are completely dependent on loving adults for food, shelter, and education, but can attain free will without the same support?

People who lack security become frightened, cannot think clearly, and abdicate reason for quick and simple solutions. Locked in a sense of hopelessness and helplessness, many are overcome by fear and anger, and are deprived of two foundations necessary for free will—a sense of belonging and the opportunity to dream.

The day will come when we see that the range and reach of mental illness is stunningly greater than we now know. Even the experts among you who declare that there was understanding of right and wrong have not yet begun to fathom how the mind works, though certainty pervades their opinions. Today, many are unable to navigate life because of unknown mental disorders, just as in days past many felt the brunt of punishment because of physical disorders that were not understood at the time. Experts of the past asserted that the different ones were evil, and certainty pervaded their opinions also.

> False certainty pervades,
> and feels as firm and comforting as the ground,
> but true certainty eludes.
> When we believe we are certain, we reach for
> the wind.

True scholars are ever mindful of the impossibility of certainty and the certainty of mistakes.

Few of you realize how difficult it is for so many to become full and complete persons, who can control their impulses and make good choices, because for you, it wasn't difficult—you had the three foundations.

Any action based on the perception of inherent evil is inherently wrong, for the miscreant is driven by influences far beyond our present understanding. Though it may seem strange, one day we will see that people do the best they can with the hand they are dealt, and there are many parts of that hand we cannot see.

We must forgive people for being the only thing they can be.

As we have surrendered the centrality of the earth in the universe in the Copernican understanding, and the uniqueness of humanity in evolution, so we must surrender some of our conception of free will to understand why there is evil and how to prevent it.

THE LISTENER THEN SAID, SPEAK TO US OF JUSTICE AND PUNISHMENT.

AND WITH THE experience of life, he said: Here, perhaps I ask the most of you. You believe that punishment, and the fear of it, will change or deter those who do wrong. This belief is natural and understandable because in normal circumstances, people are deterred by unpleasant consequences, but here it is not so simple.

My brothers and sisters, in this matter, we must see with both our hearts and our minds. We cannot ask aggrieved individuals to understand, but we as a people must realize collectively that punishment is very limited in its ability to prevent evil, for evildoers are victims of an unseen roll of the dice that leaves them unable to exercise good judgment. Those who have done wrong are not people of a fundamentally different type who can be punished, removed, or killed as we might remove weeds from a garden. They are part of humanity, and less responsible for their actions than it appears. Unless disturbed by mental illness, fear, a lack of opportunities, or an absence of discernible and accessible alternatives, the human mind is not violent or evil. The last, the least, and the lost include those who have wronged us, and prevention is the only deterrent.

Anger and a desire for revenge are understandable responses to a terrible event, but I am hopeful that a desire for revenge will not long control our thoughts or determine our actions. I am hopeful for a time when hate is not met with hate, when cruelty is not met with cruelty, but when both are met with reason, understanding, and with a belief that all life has value. I am hopeful for a time when we help each other reach a new world where "an eye for an eye" is replaced with understanding and mercy, and accountability is tempered with awareness of the myriad uncontrollable, unknowable variables in the long process of becoming a person.

In matters of evil and justice, certainty of punishment is more important than severity of punishment, and prevention of the conditions that promote evil behavior is more important than either.

And if a terrible event does occur, let us strive not for revenge, but for rapid and permanent closure. Severe punishment offers revenge that is temporarily sweet, but mercy and rapid closure offer a far better pathway to recovery. Let us not think of what the *perpetrator deserves,* but of what *allows a loving society to heal* as quickly and completely as possible.

The ways of the past are familiar and comforting, but new ways offer limitless possibilities. If we turn to the future and listen, we can hear a soft whisper that the gentle hand brings more prevention than the iron fist; that punishment diminishes us all, and disturbs the spirit of those yet to come; that the anger and hate of punishment only augment the anger and hate of the crime. That whisper can guide us away from the poverty of retribution and toward the fullness of transformation.

Of course we want justice, a setting right of the wrong, a decisive shout that we will not have evil.

But let us have accountability without vengeance.
Let us have an affirmation of right and wrong without hate.

Let us help victims without creating more victims, for the loved ones of the punished perpetrators grieve as surely as the loved ones of the victims.

Once understanding of right and wrong is undermined by an invisible hand that disrupts humanity, normal deterrents cannot be recognized. The threat of punishment sends a message that cannot be received, because those we would punish are disturbed in ways unseen, and cannot control their lives or plan a future. When you punish, you cut the top of the weed without regard to the root that spawned it.

Most in your jails have not committed a violent crime, and many who languish there have not been convicted of anything. Their humanity has been taken, and their families shattered, simply because they could not pay bail, making many of your jails effectively debtors' prisons. "Innocent until proven guilty" has become guilty until proven affluent.

If this goes on, the day will come when half of you incarcerate the other half, still convinced that punishment changes the weed into the flower.

There are people who must be segregated because they are a threat to others, but they are a minority of the incarcerated, and preemptive measures would have prevented many

of these situations. Even in these cases, the goal should be to
protect others by segregating, not punishing, the individual.

> Lack of nurturing interactions
> largely caused the behavior.
> How can more deprivation improve it?

Denial of humanity cannot make a better human. Trying
to restore humanity with deprivation is watering a parched
flower with dust.

> As much as possible, be kind to those who are
> incarcerated.
> A drop of kindness saturates the roots of
> humanity,
> but cruelty only sharpens the thorn.

> Give those who must be incarcerated
> skills for life and employment,
> tools to use,
> something to hope for.
> Give them animals to whom they can be kind,
> and contact and correspondence with others
> who are not confined,
> so that they can feel a sense of belonging,

for kindness and belonging illuminate better choices.

Punishment and deterrence cannot work unless they are coupled to an alternative that is both foreseeable and attainable. If you punish without giving the offender a means of reentering society, he will be forever alienated and therefore forever prone to recidivism.

Do not allow the rare individual who partakes of your kindness and repeats harm to change your thinking, for there will always be a few who will harm again. Here is the way to minimize that number.

Some will call this naïveté, but recognition of failure and awareness of ignorance is the finest of wisdom. Do we really believe that recognizing failure is naïve? Do we really believe that charity and kindness and mercy and foresight are naïve? Are we so overcome by emotion that we will not allow reason, the singular and precious gift of our species, to be heard?

It is difficult to grasp the superiority of these ideas because it takes time to alter the lives of the invisibly ill and deprived, and these ideas have never been given sufficient time to bear fruit.

The past casts a long shadow on individuals and on societies, so we must think in the long term and our patience must be great.

We are the only species that can analyze, reason, think in the long term, and change our behavior, but these gifts remain elusive for us.

Be ever mindful that always there will be much that we do not know. Until the march of science finally casts its iridescent glow on mental illness and illuminates the myriad enigmas of the mind, we must realize that certainty is elusive and free will illusory.

We may not see the day when this glow brings us understanding, but the ability to anticipate it, and the mercy of the human heart, are humanity at its best.

We need not wait for understanding to have compassion.

Mercy mitigates ignorance and minimizes its damage. Vengeance exacerbates ignorance and magnifies its damage. Mercy allows humanity to shine, and a better future to unfold, even when understanding is incomplete. Vengeance allows incomplete understanding to diminish humanity.

The illusion of perfect knowledge is your enemy. Most errors of judgment, and most tragedies of history, result from certainty of knowledge. You must guard against this in matters of war and justice.

THE DEPARTURE

ALMUSTAFA THEN TURNED to his ship. He said: My friends, this visit is but a single day, for I must return, as must you. Our lives call us all. Feel sadness at my departure, as do I, but mourn me not, for I will dwell in your thoughts and remain in your lives.

The course of your life, and your gift to your children, depends upon the firmness with which you grasp only a few simple principles. Remember always the first principles of love, kindness, hope, and curiosity. Turn to them for solace and contentment in any storm.

Love transforms us from the mundane to the sublime. With love, we step into a better world and live in a better way. Love is always transcendent and triumphant.

All forms of love enrich us. Passion is a form of love that gives us direction in life, meaning, a reason to be excited and happy. A reason to simply be.

Our world needs kindness because all of us are helpless at the beginning and end of our lives, and many more times in between than we realize. We are sculptors of each other's lives. Go into the world and sculpt others with a kind heart and gentle hands.

The sparkling celestial radiance of kindness, given and received, makes life worth living.

> Hope is the gift of life, the enabler of life.
> Hope lives beside fear and is never diminished
> by it.
> Hope offers respite from loneliness and fills us
> with gladness.
> Even in loneliness and fear, if you have some-
> thing to hope for, you have life in all its fullness.

Curiosity opens the doors of the world and fills us with the wonderment of a child. Curiosity connects us to the universe from which we arose, to which we will return, and from which we never separate.

Make the first principles of love, kindness, hope, and curiosity your compass as you navigate the storms of life. If you hold them firmly, the storms cannot permanently wound you. These great pillars will fill you with purpose and allow you to rise up to life instead of being beaten down by it.

With them, a new world is within your grasp, and before the hourglass of eternity empties much more, you can give to your children a whole new world, based on love.

Use first principles to strive for richness. Through them, you will find your own voice, and that voice will be your unique signature in the universe, even if it is a whisper that few will hear.

Nature gives every species a unique ability, which it must use to the fullest to survive. Ours is foresight and the ability to see with the mind what cannot be seen with the eye. The one uniquely human gift is that we are the only species whose progeny can be happier because of our deliberate choices, but for this to happen, we must address problems with farsighted thinking, not with immediate reactions and expedient solutions. We must understand why problems arise, and think in the long term to solve them.

Our progress is constrained by three limitations: lack of curiosity; lack of foresight; and lack of empathy. Lack of foresight obscures the larger lesson that always looms in a setback, causing us to take baby steps instead of giant steps.

Understanding always works, though it takes time.
Ignorance always fails, though its simplicity may temporarily comfort, concealing the failure.
Even the best leadership never changes this.
Leadership can be wonderful, but it is only as good as the understanding on which it is based.
Scholarship and patience are the foundations of leadership.

People who can understand the present and look ahead with both mind and heart improve the world and shape the future.

The world is full of ignorance, but not of stupidity, evil, or cruelty. You will suffer from the ignorance of others, past and present, but you will primarily suffer from your own un-suspected ignorance. It is better to recognize your own igno-rance and learn, than to be angry at the ignorance of others.

Human nature and the human experience do not funda-mentally change from one time to another. We do not live very different lives from people in any other time or place. Be happy with the time and place allotted you.

Though unforeseen moments may bring us sadness, we are often given unexpected pleasures and opportunities. All of our lives are mixtures of happiness and sadness, prosperity and poverty, belonging and loneliness. Accept all of these as the glittering threads that tie you to your fellow travelers and allow you to bask in the subtle yet infinite richness of life.

Feel the basic gentleness of the breeze, even amidst the occasional gust. Take in as much of the world's goodness, in all of its forms, as you can, and add to it whenever you can, in any way you can.

Be proud of your past, even if you made mistakes. Be happy with the present, even if it is not perfect. Have hope for the future, even if it is uncertain.

Be liberated by hope, not imprisoned by fear.

Be guided by the wisdom of the past and inspired by the promise of the future. Strive for a legacy of influence, not accomplishment.

The circle of life gives to you when you give, teaches you when you teach, and brings you respite when you comfort.

Always, you will have desires, but you hold in your heart that which is essential to happiness, and you hold in your hand the gift of happiness to others. Take pleasure in life as it is, for what it is.

Beauty is all around you, flitting unseen in many forms. To see it in its majesty, you need only pause, step away from the mundane, and think and see and wonder with the mind of a child—and there it will be.

Do not seek beauty; unveil it. Do not seek love; open your mind and your heart and let it find you.

Each one of you matters, even in the eternity of time and the infinity of space. Be proud of who you are and what you have done. Feel the earth beneath you, look at the sky above you, and feel the welcoming embrace of the universe.

Do not be discouraged by the pace of progress or occasional relapses. Collectively, we must pass through stages of development, as we do individually. Each stage takes time, and can no more be rushed than a child can be made to grow faster. In moments of setback, do not despair, but take heart in the good, as the half-full glass can still quench your thirst.

Though the dawn has not come, darkness abates. Victory comes slowly and unevenly, but time will bring us understanding as surely as it brings sunrises.

Humanity is neither good nor bad, but some of both as we continue to mature. We are a work in progress, not a completed work that is defective.

Believe in the primacy of kindness and the progress of humanity. Believe that tomorrow's history will be better than today's past.

MANY ASKED: WILL YOU RETURN?

*A*ND HE SAID: I am not leaving you. Though my body is separated from yours, our minds remain embraced in love and thought. As long as the heart of humanity beats with the hope for a better world, I will dwell among you.

If you remember this day, the sweet dawn of the rising sun will cast comforting shadows in your lives, and its shimmering supernal glow will radiate within you.

Then he boarded, and as calm seas took the prophet home, his ship again became a speck on the horizon, leaving the people with sadness and sorrow. But as the speck became smaller, sadness gave way to memories, and sorrow gave way to wisdom, and the people of Orphalese returned to lives made richer.